THIS LAND WE DEFEND

THIS LAND WE DEFEND

BY

HUGH HAMMOND BENNETT

and

WILLIAM CLAYTON PRYOR

Illustrated with photogravures

LONGMANS, GREEN AND CO.

NEW YORK · TORONTO

BENNETT & PRYOR

THIS LAND WE DEFEND

PUBLISHED SIMULTANEOUSLY IN
THE DOMINION OF CANADA BY
LONGMANS, GREEN AND CO., TORONTO

First edition September 1942
Reprinted September 1943

This complete copyright edition is produced in full compliance with the Government's regulations for conserving paper and other essential materials.

PRINTED IN THE UNITED STATES OF AMERICA

To

James Paul Buchanan

of Texas

1867–1937

Who Early Recognized the Great Value of

America's Soil Resource

and

Was Instrumental in Launching

the Nation on a course of

Practical Soil Conservation

PREFACE

THIS NATION IS AT WAR.

That is a fact which we dare not minimize. It means that we must put every ounce of our energy into the effort to win. We've got to see that every available ingot of iron goes into armaments—that every bit of food goes to feed our people and our Allies so that we may have the strength to use those armaments successfully.

All our resources must be devoted to the war. All the products of our mines and laboratories, of our forests and farms must be spent for victory. All our basic resources must be conserved to that end. We must make victory inevitable.

This won't be easy. With war spreading all about us like wildfire around the world, many of us thought its angry flames could never leap the oceans and burn us. But we were wrong.

We changed the subject when the war was mentioned. We dilly-dallied with defense. Then suddenly, on a Sunday about dinner time, we were at war. Immediately we rolled up our sleeves and pitched in, trying to make up overnight for the deficiencies in our defenses—the gaps in our armor which we had permitted by our carelessness and procrastination.

There is a striking parallel between our war effort and the nation's fight to save one of our basic resources so vital to national defense—the soil. We didn't believe the signs of erosion danger either.

Now we are plunged into the midst of bitter living history, to win or lose according to the earnestness of our effort.

This is the situation: We are opposing our enemies' tanks and planes, their ships and guns, with our own tanks and planes and ships and guns. We are fighting the enemy's supply of foodstuffs from the "slave-operated" farms of the conquered countries with the foodstuffs from our own farms, produced by our own free people.

Our job now is two-fold: to fight, and to help feed the forces of the United Nations that need our help throughout the world—and after the war perhaps to help feed all humanity that may need it. It's been said often and by many people that "America is the hope of the world"—the soil of the farms of America is essential to the realization of that hope.

We must win the war on *every* front—here and abroad.

CONTENTS

LIST OF ILLUSTRATIONS

MAPS

THIS LAND WE DEFEND

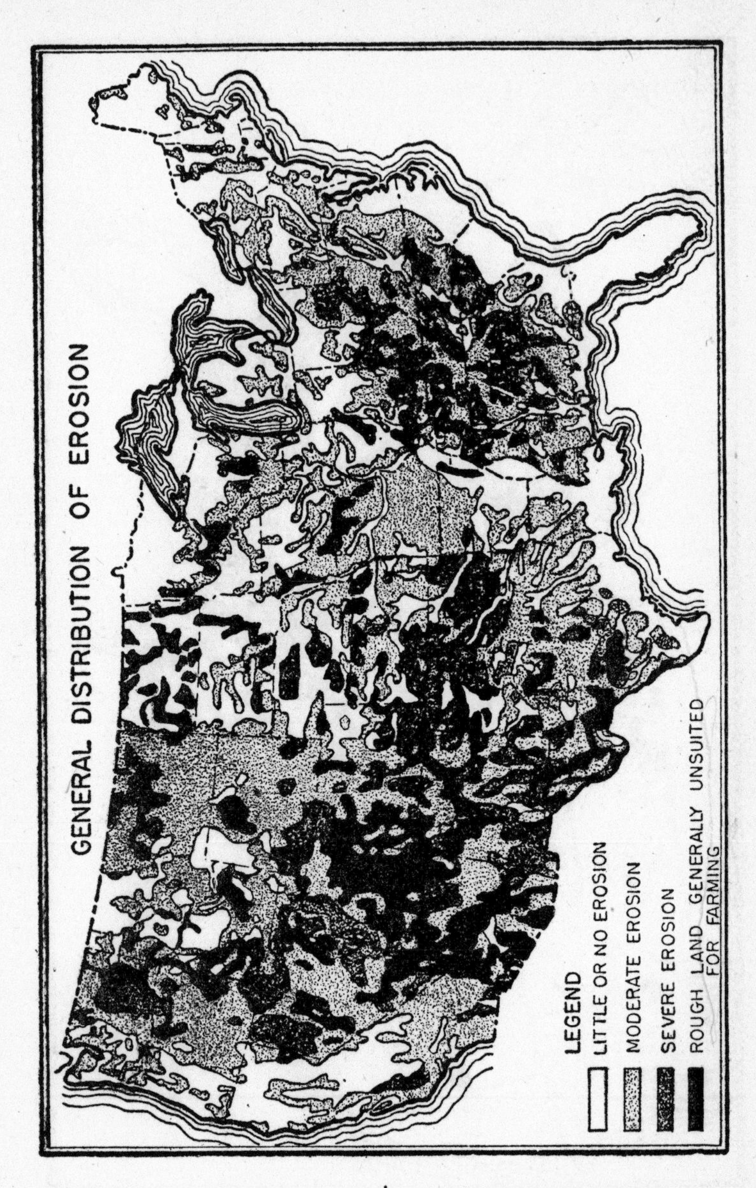
GENERAL DISTRIBUTION OF EROSION
LEGEND
LITTLE OR NO EROSION
MODERATE EROSION
SEVERE EROSION
ROUGH LAND GENERALLY UNSUITED FOR FARMING

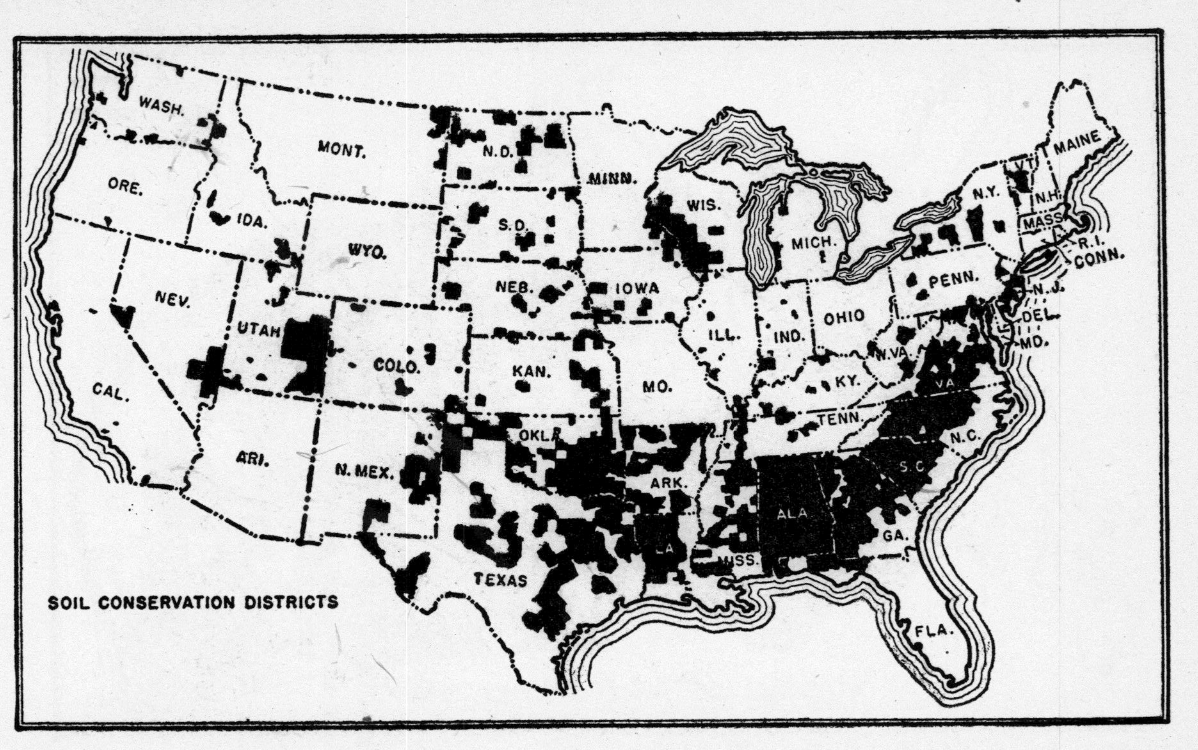

SOIL CONSERVATION DISTRICTS

CHAPTER I

AMERICA

AMERICA IS BEAUTIFUL.

America is free.

We think these things but rarely put them into words like these. Instead—

"I like it here," we say. "I like it in the spring when plowing makes the earth smell fresh and fragrant and the first leaves on that line of willows by the creek make a pale green fringe around the fields. I like it in the summer when things are growing day and night, and in the autumn when all the crops are in and we have enough stored up to last us through the winter."

We say:

"America is the place to live—a place where people still have freedom. Democracy may have its faults—I guess it has—but still I don't know of any better form of government."

We say:

"America is rich—we've all it takes to make a country rich—natural resources such as mines, millions of acres of good productive land, and forests of fine timber. Not many countries have as much as we."

All those things are true: America *is* free; America does have great resources. And America can hold on to those things, not by casual acceptance but only by active defense.

First, we've got to keep this country free. Remember Lincoln's speech at Gettysburg? He hit it on the head. America's got to buckle down and handle her end so that, as Lincoln said, freedom "shall not perish from the earth."

Then, we've got to look after those natural resources that make us rich, if we want to hang on to them.

We've been a little careless in the past about our land, for one thing. We had that "get-rich-quick" idea in our heads and we worked the land to full capacity and then some. The result is, there are millions of acres of land that used to be fertile and highly productive that now are completely ruined. And a lot more on the way unless we stop it. Erosion of soil by wind and water has done that—erosion caused by overcropping and overgrazing, and misuse of land.

It seems incredible, but for almost three centuries erosion has been a constant threat to the farms of America and their owners, and to the prosperity and well-being of the nation as a whole.

And for all but the last few years of that time, despite repeated warnings from a few thoughtful men in each generation, we have taken no notice. We have permitted erosion to go on gnawing its way across our fields and pastures. Complacently we said: "Why, that's perfectly natural. A little washing is bound to occur in every field." Then we went on with our plowing.

Finally, less than a decade ago, we woke up to the fact that our topsoil was washing and blowing away, much faster than nature could replace it. And we had been doing nothing about it.

We got to work then. We knew a little about erosion and we set about learning more, and finding out how to combat it—how to repair the damage already done where that was possible, and how to protect our undamaged lands from washing and blowing.

It took us a good while to get going. It will take us a good deal longer to accomplish all that needs to be done, but at last we've started.

Soil is one of the most important—perhaps the *most* important—of our basic resources. From the farms of America come our clothing and our food—and part of the food and fiber for some other nations of the world. In time of world-wide war, the burden is greatly increased, but, war or peace, millions of people depend on American acres.

The farms, as well as the farmers, of America have,

therefore, a tremendous responsibility. We've got to keep them in shape to meet that responsibility.

It's a truism that a nation can't prosper unless its agriculture prospers. It's equally true that a nation without adequate and good soil resources, from which its people literally draw their sustenance and strength, will not have sufficient stamina to survive a long and bitter war.

The history of the eastern Mediterranean region is a case in point. In Biblical times it included many agricultural nations, with extensive irrigation systems in the plains. But the people of those days were like the people of today ; they wanted all they could get. In the highlands they cut too many trees and plowed the hillsides, and grazed too many goats. Each rainstorm washed some topsoil off and in the dry periods the wind blew it away, and it gradually filled up the irrigation ditches and stopped the flow of water.

Look at Mesopotamia. At a time in its history when a good deal of that country was not much worse off than some of our land in America is today, Mongol hordes came and laid waste the country. The Mesopotamians were unable successfully to resist. With their irrigation systems ruined by enemies or by silt from the hill country, their agriculture fell into decay. Without a vigorous agriculture they lacked stamina as a nation and fell before succeeding waves of invaders. For centuries Mesopotamia has been a land of ruin.

Such things should be a lesson to us. We're rich now — we've got all we need unless we go on wasting more and more of our good land. We're powerful, too — the most powerful nation in the world, they say.

But we may not be so rich and powerful very long, unless we keep our land — our productive soil — in place. The land is what we live on and from — it's fundamental.

That's why we've got to go "all out" to save the soil of "This Land We Defend."

CHAPTER II

LAND AND SECURITY

LAND IS MOST IMPORTANT OF ALL MAN'S MATERIAL possessions.

Without productive land man cannot have the things that are essential to his happiness and welfare, even to his life: food, shelter, clothing, health, freedom.

Food, shelter, and clothing are products of the land, and without them we could have no security. Without security there would be no freedom. This was true in the early days of man and it is equally true today.

Events of three and four centuries ago show how the unwise use of land can affect the general welfare, and indicate some of the factors that caused great numbers of Europeans to emigrate to America.

The early years of the seventeenth century in England were not happy years. As a nation England felt sharp economic pressure. There was privation among individuals.

Spain was becoming wealthy and powerful through her colonial ventures and possessions, and England feared the ascendancy of her Latin neighbor.

About this time, England – then primarily an agri-

"Millions of acres . . . completely ruined."

Sheep graze too closely, and tiny hooves cut the sod.

cultural nation — began to experience a heavy increase in the demand for wool. Here was something that *could* be produced at home on the productive land of the British Isles, and the landowners forthwith set about to make as much money as they could from wool.

Large areas of farm land that had been producing two crops — food for the nation and a living of sorts for the farm laborers — were taken out of cultivation and converted into pasture, to feed the growing flocks of sheep that bore the newly precious wool.

The inevitable result was to throw many farm laborers out of work, since fewer men were required to tend the flocks than had been needed to tend the crops. A small portion of these laborers found other work, but for the most part there was little or nothing they could do. Unskilled men could make no place for themselves in the trades, and mostly their only resources were their muscles. And muscles, even the strongest, are useful in the economic sense only when they're engaged in productive work.

Social conditions among the working classes, already bad, were made acute by economic factors far beyond the knowledge or comprehension of the idle, ignorant plowman and his hungry family. The supply of hard cash had been increased by importation. This increase in the supply of gold and silver sent prices up to where the common man could hardly afford even to wish for the necessities of life, much less buy them.

The immediate result was unfortunate. Human beings have a tremendous will to live, and the unemployed laborers resorted to any means at hand to get food for themselves and their families.

Robbers and beggars infested the narrow, ill-lighted streets of London and the provincial towns. Highwaymen waylaid the unwary traveler who rode alone along the muddy highroads between the pasture fields where lately the bandits may have worked at farming.

All this because men had been taken off the land which had fed them, clothed them and sheltered them; which had supported them and given them some security. Thus unwillingly divorced from livelihood, they obtained the necessities of life by uneconomic and illicit means. They obtained the necessities of life, but no security, no freedom. They were regarded as a vicious and a dangerous lot, outlawed, hunted, their lives constantly in jeopardy.

The science of economics being ill-understood then, statesmen thought that England was becoming overpopulated. The thing to do was to get rid of the surplus.

America, the vast continent to the west, offered a solution: Send the "surplus population" to America to establish colonies! Not only would this correct the "overpopulation problem," but at the same time England could begin to tap the riches of the new world which John Cabot had claimed for her a century before!

This is the background of the English colonization of America. A nation's struggle to forge ahead in an expanding world and a people's need for land and all it meant in security, happiness, and freedom, bore a gigantic fruit which is this land that we defend today.

Land of their own, prerequisite to all the things they held worthwhile, first of all was what these people sought.

Thus America has been from its political beginnings a land of freedom, and so it remains today. Freedom of action and expression is the keystone of the American philosophy of life and of government.

President Franklin D. Roosevelt renewed this nation's dedication to this ideal in an address when he set down as America's program: "Freedom of speech and expression, freedom of worship, freedom from want, freedom from fear."

These freedoms, this security in a world too insecure, must be preserved. And we dare not forget the source of all these things—this peace, security, and freedom:

Foremost and fundamental is the preservation of the land.

CHAPTER III

THE NEW WORLD

THREE SMALL SAILING VESSELS MOVED SLOWLY UP A broad tidewater river. Aboard the ships there was rejoicing, for it was a bright May day and six months of battling the bitter Atlantic winter were at an end.

The dense forests and the lush meadows along both banks seemed to bear out the reports of Captain Arthur Barlow to Sir Walter Raleigh after the explorations of 1584: "The soile is the most plentifull, sweete, fruitfull and wholesome of all the worlde."

As quickly as a suitable spot was found, the ships tied up and men swarmed ashore. Almost their first activity was to build a fort to defend themselves. Then a church; then a storehouse; and then log huts for homes.

Then they plowed the land, and planted seed to grow their food.

This was in the year of 1607, in what is now Virginia.

* * *

Another ship, wracked by howling North Atlantic winter gales, rounded a curving arm of rugged land

and in its lee found calmer water. The battered vessel pounded her way along the inhospitable December coast until she found a place to anchor.

The men and women who landed there found no spring sunshine spread out for them; no luxuriant green fields, nor trees in summer dress.

But thanksgiving for their safe arrival at this bleak and wintry port armed them with courage to face the unknown future. The land itself provided them with shelter. They felled trees to build homes and church and stockade. For food they had wild game and fish.

And in the spring they plowed the land, and planted corn and other crops with the aid of friendly Indians.

This was in the winter and spring of 1620-21, in what we now call Massachusetts.

* * *

These pioneers had sailed across 3000 miles of perilous ocean to find a land where they could live in liberty and with better economic opportunity than they had at home in Europe. They came to find peace, freedom and security.

They found them, but not at once. First of all, they found the land on which through years of toil and suffering they were to build a nation. Nearly two centuries rolled across the world, six generations rose and set, before they won their liberty.

The odds these pioneers faced in America were greater than those they faced in the old world.

Here in the new world they found, besides the vast new land, new dangers. Some Indians were hostile to the colonists from the outset, and others became implacable foes as the white men encroached upon their land. Raids and massacres upon the white settlements, bloody death winging from forest ambush; diseases and death from bad water, bad food, exposure—even from starvation, now and then. For even Nature turned traitor at times, and crop failure then left the colonists in desperate plight.

But still they had the land to keep them going. It is the land that nourishes and sustains a people, and from their land the colonists drew strength and faith and courage. And eventually they found the things they came to find:

Peace and freedom, wrought and held in flesh and blood and tears.

Security, won the hard way, through toil and sweat, by aching bones and muscles.

They set up a new kind of nation in the world, born of suffering and strife, dedicated to liberty and security for all—the first great democracy in modern history.

The basic principle of democracy is the voluntary joining together of individual wills to give form and expression to the corporate will. Only through such a process can the common welfare be promoted, can a people defend itself, and protect and preserve for its posterity the land on which its freedom and security are founded.

Only a self-reliant people, sustained by man's basic resource, the soil, can make a success of democracy. The new nation had the land—more than it dreamed of—and it had a sturdy people, fired by ambition, filled with the pioneer spirit.

Necessarily the new colonies in America were largely agricultural. Most of the manufactured goods the colonists used they imported from Europe, paying for them with the produce of their farms.

Tobacco, which grew readily in the rich lands of the coastal plain, was in demand in Europe and became the colonists' medium of exchange for manufactured articles. So they grew tobacco, crop after crop, year after year, and sent it to England,

Crop after crop, year after year, tobacco drained the riches from the land along the coast and left it exhausted, with thousands of sloping acres slashed by the rains.

Thus early in our country's history was the chapter

on soil exhaustion and erosion begun. Farmers in tight little European countries had no room for expansion, so they took good care of what land they had. But America was different.

Here there was more land to the west, and west the people went. Farmers, finding their land impoverished, left it and moved from the coast up into the foothills — the Piedmont country — to mine the wealth from out *that* soil, and then move on still farther west. They crossed the valleys and easterly ranges into the Appalachian Plateau, plowed the land and took from it all they could, and again moved on.

This westward movement was a pageant of decades and centuries, not just a few years. For a century, in fact, the Appalachians remained the frontier of the new American nation.

Throughout that time, only the adventurous crossed their folded ridges bathed in blue. Daniel Boone, Simon Kenton—and forgotten families, holding tight their courage and their muskets — these blazed the trail that civilization was to follow.

The stories these adventurers brought back — or sent — told of the amazing richness of the land beyond the mountains; forest-clad hills and lush valleys, teeming with life on the ground and the very stuff of life beneath.

"Tobacco drained the riches from the land."

Virgin grasslands in Wyoming, 1873

They set new dreams to whirling within the minds of men. Here was a land of richness beyond imagining, waiting to be taken, when once the people had accomplished the winning of a war and the founding of a nation.

When these things were done, the westward flow of civilization was resumed.

Then men moved on, pushing before them toward the distant Pacific, the western frontier of the newborn nation.

CHAPTER IV

MARCH OF THE EXPLOITERS

UP THE HUDSON AND THE MOHAWK.

Across the Appalachians and down the Ohio.

Through the Cumberland Gap and out the Wilderness Road.

In ever-swelling numbers the pioneers pushed west, in flatboats and in Conestoga wagons, on horseback and on foot:

West to the Mississippi, west to the Plains, west to the Rockies.

Pushing the wilderness before them, making new trails as they went:

The Oregon Trail and the Overland Trail.

The Utah Trail, and the California Trail with gold at the end.

The Santa Fe Trail and the old Spanish Trail.

Like a giant fan, the westward trek of civilization left its mark upon the land.

On they came from the East, and on they went to the West, blazing new trails, making new roads, laying iron rails behind them.

For there was immeasurable wealth in this vast new land and every man of them meant to have his share.

This is the story of the winning of the West; this is the story of America's expansion.

It is also the story of exploitation—of a people who almost killed the goose that laid the golden eggs.

By the time the Revolutionary War ended there were scattered pioneer settlements between the Appalachians and the Mississippi, but the great river was then the American frontier.

The area west of Pittsburgh and east of the river was becoming farming country as rapidly as men could cut the giant trees, clear out the stumps, and plow the land.

The farmer was the real pioneer of what we now call the Middle West. He it was—usually with a hard-working wife and an increasing family—who rooted out the wilderness and established civilization in the region.

This was hard work. Trees had to be cut and stumps dug out. Often, when all the logs needed for a cabin and perhaps a crude stable had been cut, clearing was done more simply. They girdled the trees and when they were dead, they burned them.

It was a terrific waste. Great logs of oak, black walnut, hickory, birch, and other valuable trees were burned everywhere—timber that would bring millions upon millions of dollars at today's prices.

But that was all right. There were plenty of trees—

too many for the pioneer farmers who wanted cleared land to grow their crops. And so they cleared the land the easiest and quickest way they could.

This land that had produced mighty stands of timber which early explorers found "farre greater and better" than those of Europe, produced fabulous farm crops, too.

Year after year, crop after crop, the farmers worked the land, as their ancestors had done in the Tidewater and Piedmont regions east of the mountains.

If, after several years of growing corn continuously, a field became sterile, it didn't matter. There was plenty of land in this great continent—more than would ever be used.

And so the farmer cleared another field, and let the rains wash the top off that as well as his abandoned acres—down the gullies to the creek, down the creek to the river, down the river to the sea.

While the farmer-pioneer was thus establishing civilization in the Middle West, and towns and villages were springing up, centers of provincial trade and frontier culture, the adventurers pushed on farther west.

Beyond the Mississippi for the most part lay an unknown region. Spanish and French soldiers, missionaries and fur-traders knew it, but they were about the only ones. It was a land of Indians who, having been evicted from their eastern homes, were now definitely hostile to the white men. It was a land of wild animals and unknown dangers.

It was a land, some thought, of unknown riches, too. There was much speculation concerning it, and President Thomas Jefferson was one of those who was deeply interested in the vast area included in the Louisiana Purchase.

In 1804 he despatched Meriwether Lewis and William Clark to explore the region of the upper Missouri River.

In 1805 he sent Zebulon Pike to find the source of the Mississippi itself, and in 1806 to find the sources of the Arkansas and the Red rivers. Pike found no river sources but he came back from the first expedition with information about the region which is now Minnesota and Wisconsin, and from his second with a great deal of data about a vast area of the Southwest, then under Spanish rule.

In 1806 Lewis and Clark returned from the Northwest with a story of burning heat on arid deserts, plains reaching from horizon to horizon, of bitter winter in mountains which made the Appalachians look like grassy knolls, of lush fertile lands beyond the Continental Divide. It was a report of vast herds of buffalo on the plains, of nomadic Indian tribes who ranged the west and lived largely on the buffaloes and other game they killed. It was the story of a trail of hardship and death, with rich farm country at the end.

Other adventurers sailed around South America to the west coast, to California and to Oregon, but for a time the westward movement proceeded slowly.

The rich valley of the Mississippi gradually filled with people. Most of the forest disappeared, the grass-lands of the prairie country were broken out, and cultivated fields took their place. Presently the valley became so "crowded" that villages sprang up here and there less than a dozen miles apart.

Then people began to complain of the "lack of opportunity" and "too much competition." There was more land, more opportunity farther west.

Faces were turned again toward the distant Rockies and feet once more were set on the westward trails. Only the hardier few at first, until one day in January, 1848, a New Jersey emigrant's pick, digging a ditch in California, struck gold.

Gold!

The shout and echo had hardly died away among the California hills until the word was hurrying east as fast as men could carry it.

Gold in California! Gold in the Rockies! Gold in the West!

The words were potent magic to thousands, and people feverishly took to the road: adventurers, malcontents who did not get along with their neighbors, criminals seeking regions where they would not be restricted by law; single men, men with wives and young children; farmers, laborers, artisans, business men, professional men.

They dropped their plows and hammers, they closed their stores and offices and homes. They packed the essentials of existence into as small a space as possible and started west.

They hurried to the nearest river landing. Steamboats down the Ohio, steamboats up and down the Mississippi, steamboats up the Missouri, to Independence, loaded to the gunwales with humanity and provisions, picks and shovels and guns.

Independence, a small frontier outpost one week; a crowded, boisterous, expensive, unpleasant boom town the next; the last "jumping-off place" for the uncharted west and riches!

From Independence west by many trails the people moved in ever growing numbers. In lumbering "prairie schooners," on horseback, on foot with their belongings on their backs or in wheelbarrows, they set out across the most difficult two-thirds of the continent, to find their fortunes.

It was an amazing spectacle: a pageant of human greed and of human courage; a pageant of exploitation, a pageant of suffering, and sometimes of unselfish sacrifice.

While this overland march was on, still others went by sea. Thirty-five thousand "forty-niners" reached California by ship in 1849, and 42,000 more by land.

A few of them found the gold they went for: rich placers—nuggets as big as their fists, and gold dust in the gravel beds of mountain streams. Others, failing these, found their gold in the produce of rich agricultural lands and forests; still others in trading with their fellow-adventurers.

Some of them found death before they reached trail's end. Some stopped in Idaho, and others left the California Trail at Fort Bridger, Wyoming, and pushed across to the Snake River and down the Columbia to Oregon and Washington.

Brigham Young led his Mormons west through more than a thousand miles of hardship to establish an ecclesiastical and economic empire in mountainous Utah.

And still across the west they moved, leaving a thin layer of civilization behind them on the land, from which grew villages and towns and states.

CHAPTER V

ERA OF EXPANSION

THREE GREAT WAVES OF IMMIGRATION SWEPT THE mighty West in the nineteenth century.

First, on the cry of gold, came the miners. They brought a rough-and-tumble sort of civilization, and where any semblance of law-and-order was to be found it was chiefly of a "homemade" variety. Often it was in the hands of committees of Vigilantes whose efforts were sometimes as illegal as the excesses they tried to control. Sometimes one man was "the law," as was the case with "Judge" Roy Bean of Texas, famous in his time as "the Law west of the Pecos."

After the miners came the cattlemen. The cowboy became a figure of romance equal to the pony express rider and the driver of the Overland stage. These dashing lean riders herded their Texas longhorns throughout the West from the Missouri to the Rockies, from the Mexican border to the Canadian line, and gave life in the plains country the same violent flavor the miners gave it in the mountains.

Then came the farmers and their families and drove the cattlemen on into the western plains and the foothills of the Rockies.

At the peak of the cattle era in the Plains states, pioneers of a different turn of mind had started laying steel rails west. The Union Pacific Railway was completed to the Pacific coast in 1869, annihilating distance and bringing civilization to the wilderness in a cloud of smoke and steam and a clatter of steel. By 1884 six railroads crossed the United States.

The westward rush increased in intensity. Now a man could go west and take his family along in comparative safety and comfort. The United States government had opened up federal lands to "homesteading," and the railroads had received large grants of land from the government, which they were eager to dispose of.

Every passenger west meant a ticket sold. Theoretically, every settler taken west and put on the land meant future business for the railroad: freight on western produce going east to market; freight on manufactured goods coming west for the settlers. So the railroads put on lavish advertising campaigns to urge the farmers to move west and take up land in the vast new areas now opened up.

The farmers read the glowing words and, liking the idea of easy money as well as the next fellow, went west in swelling numbers again. Some of them got good land and some of them didn't. But still they

IN THE GARDEN STATE OF THE WEST.

THE ILLINOIS CENTRAL RAILROAD CO., HAVE FOR SALE

1,200,000 ACRES OF RICH FARMING LANDS,

In Tracts of Forty Acres and upward on Long Credit and at Low Prices.

THE attention of the enterprising and industrious portion of the community is directed to the following statements and liberal inducements offered them by the

ILLINOIS CENTRAL RAILROAD COMPANY.

which, as they will perceive, will enable them, by proper energy, perseverance and industry, to provide comfortable homes for themselves and families, with, comparatively speaking, very little capital.

LANDS OF ILLINOIS.

No State in the Valley of the Mississippi offers so great an inducement to the settler as the State of Illinois. There is no portion of the world where all the conditions of climate and soil so admirably combine to produce those two great staples, CORN and WHEAT, as the Prairies of Illinois.

EASTERN AND SOUTHERN MARKETS.

These lands are contiguous to a railroad 700 miles in length, which connects with other roads and navigable lakes and rivers, thus affording an unbroken communication with the Eastern and Southern markets.

RAILROAD SYSTEM OF ILLINOIS.

Over $100,000,000 of private capital have been expended on the railroad system of Illinois. Inasmuch as part of the income from several of these works, with a valuable public fund in lands, go to diminish the State expenses; the TAXES ARE LIGHT, and must consequently every day decrease.

THE STATE DEBT.

The State debt is only $10,106,398 14, and within the last three years has been reduced $2,959,746 80, and we may reasonably expect that in ten years it will become extinct.

PRESENT POPULATION.

The State is rapidly filling up with population; 868,025 persons having been added since 1850, making the present population 1,723,663, a ratio of 102 per cent. in ten years.

AGRICULTURAL PRODUCTS.

The Agricultural Products of Illinois are greater than those of any other State. The products sent out during the past year exceeded 1,500,000 tons. The wheat crop of 1860 approaches 35,000,000 bushels, while the corn crop yields not less than 140,000,000 bushels.

FERTILITY OF THE SOIL.

Nowhere can the industrious farmer secure such immediate results for his labor as upon these prairie soils, they being composed of a deep rich loam, the fertility of which is unsurpassed by any on the globe.

Pamphlets descriptive of the lands, soil, climate, production to

J. W.

For the names of the Towns, Villages and Cities situ
469 and 170 Appleton's Railway Guide.

HOMES FOR T
(Advertising cut widely used by the Illi

"... Glowing words ..."

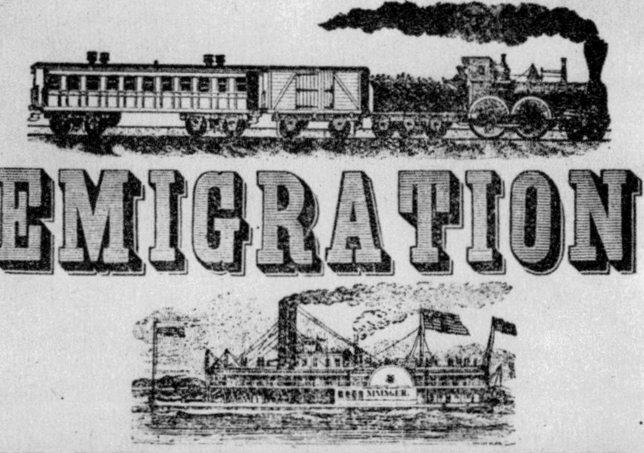

UP THE MISSISSIPPI RIVER.

The attention of Emigrants and the Public generally, is called to the now rapidly improving

TERRITORY OF MINNESOTA,

Containing a population of 150,000, and goes into the Union as a State during the present year. According to an act of Congress passed last February, the State is munificently endowed with Lands for Public Schools and State Universities, also granting five per cent. on all sales of U. S. Lands for Internal Improvements. On the 3d March, 1857, grants of Land from Congress was made to the leading Trunk Railroads in Minnesota, so that in a short time the trip from New Orleans to any part of the State will be made in from two and a half to three days. The

CITY OF NININGER,

Situated on the Mississippi River, 35 miles below St. Paul, is now a prominent point for a large Commercial Town, being backed by an extensive Agricultural, Grazing and Farming Country; has fine streams in the interior, well adapted for Milling in all its branches; and Manufacturing **WATER POWER** to any extent.

Mr. JOHN NININGER, (a Gentleman of large means, ideas and liberality, speaking the various languages,) is the principal Proprietor of **Nininger**. He laid it out on such principles as to encourage all **MECHANICS**, Merchants, or Professions of all kinds, on the same equality and footing: the consequence is, the place has gone ahead with such rapidity that it is now an established City, and will annually double in population for years to come.

Persons arriving by Ship or otherwise, can be transferred without expense to Steamers going to Saint Louis; or stop at Cairo, and take Railroad to Dunleith (on the Mississippi). Steamboats leave Saint Louis and Dunleith daily for **NININGER**, and make the trip from Dunleith in 36 to 48 hours.

NOTICES.

1. All Railroads and Steamboats giving this card a conspicuous place, or *gratuitous insertion* in their cards, AIDS THE EMIGRANT and forwards their own interest.

2. For authentic documents, reliable information, and all particulars in regard to Occupations, Wages, Preëmpting Lands (in neighborhood), Lumber, Price of Lots, Expenses, &c., apply to

THOMAS B. WINSTON, 27 Camp street, New Orleans.
ROBERT CAMPBELL, St. Louis.
JOSEPH B. FORBES, Dunleith.

Land advertising about 1860

kept on, because there was land out there—millions of acres of it, so cheap you couldn't afford not to grab off a section for yourself!

This was the story of territorial expansion. This expansion helped increase the demand for certain types of fabricated goods. Industry boomed.

Agriculture boomed, too. In 1875 the farmers had 44½ million mouths to feed instead of 23 millions as in 1850. Clear more land, put more fields in wheat and corn!

By 1900 there were 76 million mouths to feed! Plow up some more land, put in some more wheat! The farmers couldn't clear and plow their land, and plant and harvest their crops fast enough to suit them, so machinery was invented to speed up farm work.

Still the markets of America cried for more. More products of the earth, of all kinds.

Men mined the land. They mined for iron and gold and copper. They mined for corn and wheat and cotton.

Year after year, crop after crop, they mined the soil for corn and wheat and cotton. No matter if they wore out a farm completely. There was more land farther west.

And farther west they went. In a hundred years,

from 1800 to 1900, the center of population moved almost a thousand miles west, out toward the vast reservoir of "land that would never give out."

The people of the United States were a little intoxicated then with the thought of all the wealth at their disposal. They were "drunk on prospects," and they spent their prospects lavishly. All this potential wealth awaiting the axe and the pick and the plow, made men prodigal of their riches, careless of their resources.

With every year, American industry and agriculture increased their volume of production. Farming became big business. So did cattle raising.

Their business was making money. That was the big idea—the main thing. If a field was broken up by gullies, so further planting was impossible, no matter. Plenty more land! If a rancher's cattle cleaned off fifty thousand acres of range completely in one season, no matter; move on to another fifty thousand acres! There was plenty, and it was public land, open to all. The main thing was for every man to get his share of the cash. They did their best.

Year after year, the sheep and cattle clipped the rangeland clean. Crop after crop, the corn and wheat, cotton and tobacco took from the farmland its soluble resources—the plant nutrients made available by ages of soil weathering. Uncontrolled rains washed off the topsoil, then cut the slopes with gullies. Wind moved the dry, loose soil and piled it in dunes or drove it across the continent as "black dusters."

But why bother with a gullied field here and there? Or that dust blowing in early spring where wheat had grown before?

They didn't matter. America's wealth was inexhaustible, the people said, and laughed and went on plowing.

They were mistaken.

CHAPTER VI

ABUNDANCE AND WASTE

THREE HUNDRED YEARS AGO THIS COUNTRY WAS NEARLY all virgin land—hundreds of millions of acres of rich and almost untouched soil.

To the amazed white men, for centuries immured within the close confines of little European states, accustomed to farming their small tracts intensively and husbanding their soil resources carefully, it seemed limitless and inexhaustible.

Capital flowed west to speed our expansion. The men in the east who had the money knew this was a good investment. As the word flew back across the narrowing ocean to the cramped Old World, even European money flowed west to finance the exploitation of America.

Money which had to be paid back.

Well, America paid this money back—with interest—out of the virgin soil.

We paid it back, all right—out of the life-giving elements, the fabulous fertility which made our new land rich.

But we didn't pay back to the land the riches we took from it.

We cut the trees that protected the soil and we dug up the roots that held it together. We stripped the natural protective cover from our land, and forced it to yield up its riches far faster than nature could restore them.

And we put nothing back.

We robbed Peter to pay Paul, and never dreamed that some day we might have to repay Peter.

"Our natural resources are inexhaustible," we thought.

But we were wrong.

The land is still here, nearly two billion acres of it, but the top has been stripped from 282 million acres—almost completely—and is daily blowing and washing from 775 million more.

The land is still here, but there is a difference. It has been changed by reckless clearing of timber, plowing out the grasslands, overcultivation, overgrazing, and underprotection.

Heavy rains have swept across our fields and carried the fertile topsoil with them, layer after layer, down to the subsoil.

And then the subsoil, inch after inch, down to bedrock in spots.

We plowed our furrows straight and true, up and down hill, and each furrow became a sluiceway to hurry off the rainfall and topsoil. The sluiceways became rills, and the rills became small gullies. And the small gullies became huge gullies, too deep to plow over and forget, stretching their gnawing fingers into our fields, carrying away both topsoil and subsoil from our "inexhaustible" land.

In other localities, the wind lifted the dry powdery soil and bore it away.

Three billion tons of soil material washed or blown away each year: three billion dollars wasted annually.

The soil material washed and blown away in a year's time, if spread out in a blanket twelve inches thick, would cover more than 1,500,000 acres. One and a half million acres covered a foot deep: that much soil material is washed and blown away every twelve months.

The other damage that wind and water erosion causes, such as reservoirs filled, roads and bridges washed out, and wildlife destroyed, adds another $844,000,000 to the bill: a stiff price to pay for ringside seats to watch our own land washed away in the most gigantic pageant of exploitation and ruin in history.

Listen:

Three hundred years ago we had 820 million acres of virgin forest within what is now continental United States. Today that acreage has been reduced to about

630 million acres of which only 100 million acres contain timber classed as old growth—by no means all virgin stand.

Three hundred years ago there were 600 million acres of fertile grasslands. Today, only scraps of the virgin grasslands are left.

That is what we have accomplished in three short centuries—a flicker of an eye as time goes. It is a tragic accomplishment.

Of the 282 million acres already ruined or seriously damaged by erosion—15 per cent of all the land in the United States—about 270 million acres are so badly worn that they should be retired from cultivation and grazing at once.

Nearly a billion acres of crop, grazing, and forest land—more than half the total area of the country—are "sick land" or threatened land that needs treatment—heroic treatment for much of it.

And every year, at the present rate, some five hundred thousand acres of land are being ruined by wind and water erosion brought on by improper land-use practices. And tens of millions of additional acres are being damaged in some degree every year.

Most of the damage has been done in the last century. When the New Jersey emigrant's pick struck gold in California in January, 1848, this country still had most of its productive land intact. Since then we have completely ruined around 50 million acres of cropland and nearly ruined 50 million acres more; we have seriously impoverished 100 million additional acres, and have the process under way on a third 100 million acres of our farmland.

To understand fully what erosion can accomplish, look about you. Almost anywhere you travel in the United States you can see hideous examples of what happens when man fails to care for his land. North, south, east, west—waste and erosion are everywhere.

Hundreds of thousands of acres devastated in the cotton country. Raw, red gullied hillsides in the Carolinas, Georgia, Alabama, Mississippi, Tennessee, and Arkansas! They planted cotton too often there and didn't take precautions to save the soil.

The famous "black belt" of Alabama and Mississippi, a band of rich black soil extending east and west across these states, is black no longer in many places where bad farming practices have allowed the rich topsoil to wash away.

People in the western Kansas and eastern Colorado wheat lands have seen the blowing dust so thick that motorists had to use their headlights at three o'clock in the afternoon! People in California, in Wyoming, in Nebraska, in Montana, Kansas and Oklahoma—even in Michigan and New Jersey—know the effect of blowing soils. The Dakotas have had dust storms so thick that human beings had to run for shelter and almost literally barricade their doors and windows against the dust-laden wind, much as their forefathers in that wild land barricaded their cabins against marauding Indians.

Sheet erosion—in which topsoil is washed off evenly over a whole field without gullying—doesn't show up so startlingly but its effects can be—and often are—just as tragic as the more spectacular forms, and as widespread.

Agriculture, of course, is not always to blame for bad soil conditions—some of our soil was naturally poor, and in some cases industry has been the aggressor. But the ravaged areas almost all are in farming regions. Therefore conservation is of direct and personal interest to farmers and livestockmen. It is of interest, whether we know it or not, to all of us. There is not a state that hasn't its area of bad erosion, and eventually all of us feel the effect of it.

Some people dismiss the problem of erosion with the complacent assertion that it is nothing. One man's loss, they say, is another man's gain—when the topsoil washes down from the farms in the highlands it stops on the farms of the lowlands and enriches them.

That is untrue. Most of the washed soil goes down

the creeks and rivers, to pile up as silt in reservoirs, to fill up channels; some of it goes on to the sea. Blown topsoil is scattered far and wide, often over millions of acres—and laid down so thinly it probably washes away with the next big rain.

Practically all of this removed soil is gone, never to return, never to be of any use to the people of America again.

CHAPTER VII

THE COST OF PROSPERITY

In dollars alone, the cost of soil exploitation is terrific. The estimated annual bill which America pays in one way or another for erosion is $3,844,000,000. Let's look at an "itemized statement" of this staggering figure.

Three billion dollars, of course, is the "charge" for taking away three billion tons of soil material. This includes such important items as upwards of three million tons of nitrogen, almost two million tons of phosphorus, 38 million tons of potassium, 15 million tons of magnesium, 33 million tons of calcium. This is more than sixty times the quantity of these plant nutrients used in commercial fertilizer in the continental United States during one year recently, according to the National Fertilizer Association.

But there's still $844,000,000 to account for:

Almost half of this—$400,000,000—is the direct cost to the farmers of the country, through reduced farm income and forced abandonment of land left in ruin by erosion. That's a lot of money for any group to pay.

Damage caused to irrigation and drainage ditches and

to reservoirs, which become filled with eroded topsoil, comes to $63,000,000 annually throughout the United States. This is paid from public and private pocket-books.

Then there is the damage to our transportation facilities. Highways and railroads seriously damaged or washed out and harbors and navigable streams which are filled with mud or whose channels are changed or clogged account for $309,000,000 yearly when it comes to paying for repairs. And in the long run, the general public pays this bill.

The cost of general flood damage to city property, and to farm property in addition to the direct cost to farmers listed above, plus the damage to farm livestock and to wildlife comes to around $72,000,000 each year. And all of us, whether we live in country or city, have to pay our share.

All this land waste, going on unchecked for years except in a few isolated instances, is fast leaving us in a sorry state. Actually, we may one day not so far off have to face a very real land shortage in the United States. Unless we act quickly and effectively we may not have enough good soil to maintain our present living standards.

There are only about 462 million acres of really good farm land left in the United States, and of that 342

Tragedy: The aftermath of a "black duster."

"... Raw, gullied hillsides ..."

million acres already is under cultivation. The balance of 120 million acres is mostly land in grass or trees which would be suitable for cultivation but has never been plowed up. It has not been cultivated, probably, because its owners have not found it necessary or feasible to do so.

Of the 342 million acres of good land now in crops, only 62 million acres are not subject to erosion and therefore not in need of constant conservation. There is another aggregate area of 70 million acres of non-erodible land which might be made available for use, but only by judicious, far-sighted clearing, drainage or irrigation. And even that would give us only one acre of non-erodible land per capita of population—far from sufficient. Thus it becomes self-evident that we must stop the ravages of exploitation on all our natural resources.

The plight of our land is reflected in the plight of our people.

Land is our most important resource but it is important only because of what it means to people. And poor land means poor people.

Sociologists found the greatest rural unemployment and rural poverty in the southern states where erosion and other results of improper land use were particularly bad.

Poor land means poor crops.

Topsoil gone downriver doesn't make crops in the fields. Eroded, worn-out land produces low yields and often poor quality crops. Low yields mean low income and low incomes mean a low living standard, unpaid taxes, reduced trade in the community, impaired school facilities, often malnutrition, hopelessness, and migration.

Unstable land means an unstable agriculture.

No farmer is going to stay on starved land and starve his family too if he thinks there's a chance he can find a better place in some other locality. Few people will put money into land that has already started to go and will probably be all gone in a few years.

Tenancy and share-cropping are higher in the states and regions where erosion is bad than elsewhere. Many thousands of the migrant farm families who move ceaselessly over the land "following the crops" came from land that was once good but has been worn out by decades of erosion and bad land use.

And sadly enough, while erosion begets instability, instability also begets erosion. A man takes better care of that which belongs to him than he does of that which belongs to another, and thus the practices of short lease farm tenancy and share-cropping in many instances aggravate erosion and waste of natural resources.

The United States is faced with a serious and a complicated problem. It is a vital problem because it concerns our people and the source of their life, the soil. Without land, the people—and the nation—cannot survive. Part of our land is already ruined and a good deal more is on the way to ruin.

We are in a situation where action is needed—now. Conservation is the answer.

CHAPTER VIII

THE ANSWER

WHEN AMERICA WAS EXPANDING, NOT ALL THE EXpansion was westward. Into every corner of this vast and fertile continent the pioneers and their descendants moved.

Some of them went north into the timber country. Some of them settled on the slopes and in the valleys of the Appalachian Mountains. Others established farms on the bottom-lands of numerous streams, and along the sun-warmed coastal plains of the South.

Where they stopped, they settled. Where they settled, they lived and had their children, and plowed their acres and grew their crops, and took from the soil all they could force it to give.

There many of their children and their children's children stayed, and they in their turn farmed the land. Often they farmed the land too hard, leaving the fertile slopes and valleys ravished and barren; leaving the land poor for the next crop and for the next generation.

Today thousands of descendants of these sturdy pioneers of two centuries and more ago live on land that can hardly support them. This land should have come down to them from their forefathers as a reservoir of natural wealth, a heritage guarded and to be guarded for posterity. Instead it came too often as a worn-out stretch of washed and barren subsoil.

Their land is bad, but it is not all beyond improvement—it can be built up—some of it—if proper steps are taken. On such a place lives a farmer whom we will call Fred Johnson (although this is not his name), descended from pioneers of two hundred years ago. Fred Johnson's farm is not his own. Many years ago, partly as a result of careless farming practices and soil erosion, the family lost its land, and now he is a tenant farmer.

Fred Johnson lives with his wife and eight children in an unpainted three-room house on a 120-acre farm in one of the southern states, paying $40 a year rent for the place, the years he makes that much.

Unfortunately, he doesn't always make that much. In 1938, his total income from his cash crop—cotton, of course—was $29.11. After paying the landlord $29 and spending the eleven cents for something for the family at a grocery in the county seat, he was still $11 behind in his rent.

The farm Johnson is supposed to pay $40 a year rental on is typical of the sort of place thousands of American farm families are trying to make a living from.

In the front room of the house, which most of us would call a "shack," are two beds, a pair of decrepit chairs, and a fireplace that smokes so badly it's only used when absolutely necessary.

In the middle room are three beds, and nothing else, for two excellent reasons: there isn't space for another stick of furniture, and there's no money to buy it.

The third and rear room is the kitchen, dining room, and living room. There is a wood-burning kitchen stove, an old dining room table, a small unfinished table, old chairs and boxes for ten people to sit on, a battered cupboard, some crude shelves—and nothing else.

The roof leaks over the entire house. When the weather is rainy, it's pretty tough. Still, the Johnsons have shelter.

Two of the children are not yet of school age, and the two oldest never finished. The four who are now going to school don't go all the time because there isn't enough warm, decent clothing to go around. So they take turns wearing the good shoes and the best overalls and sweaters. But at any rate, they have clothing—they're not naked.

The family diet was not worked out by any nutrition expert. Here is a fairly typical supper as actually served: black-eyed peas cooked with fat back, a loaf of bread, some sorghum molasses, milk from a cow they had managed to save from the economic wreckage, and raw peanuts which they grew in considerable quantities. No green vegetables, no fruit, no fresh meat. Still, they have enough to fill their stomachs twice a day.

The farm itself is just the sort of place you'd expect after seeing the house. Only 30 acres of the 120 are under cultivation, and most of that shouldn't be. The Johnson place is in hill country, and generations of bad land use and abuse of the other natural resources of the region have left the whole area in a sorry state. On the drive from the county seat to the Johnson farm you see gullies so big you could drop that three-room house in them, level it over with dirt, and not leave even a hump.

A look at the two cotton fields that yielded one small bale explains the $29.11 cash income. One of them is close to the house and slopes down toward a little stream. It is cut with small gullies. Johnson has tossed a few pine boughs in these gullies, but that is all.

The other cotton field is about a half mile from the house on higher ground. The slope isn't quite so sharp here, but the rows invariably run up and down hill. The topsoil runs only one way.

His cornfield is even worse. It is on a pretty steep hillside, and you can guess how the rows run. This hillside has been cleared only a year but already the top is at least half gone. The corn itself is a discouraging sight. Most of it is poor and scraggly and apparently about half had not even developed any ears.

The peanuts and the little patch of black-eyed peas are the only crops that seemed to thrive. They are grown in several small low fields near the stream.

Johnson knows what the trouble is. He knows he is trying to make crops on what practically amounts to nothing but subsoil in most places and a pretty thin sifting of that over rock in some spots.

"All those fields are about worn out," he said, as one bending to the inevitable, "so I guess I'll have to clear me a patch over yonder on that hill this winter. If I can get her cleared in time I'll make me a crop next year sure."

Johnson knows what the trouble is, but he doesn't know what to do about it. He planned to clear the hillside of its considerable stand of second growth trees, and plow it up. The next year he would have to clear another. And another, and so on, until—unless something intervened—the whole 120 acres would be a desolated spot which only thousands of years of nature's sure but slow processes could rebuild to its original condition.

Conservation?

"Yes sir. Seems to me the county agent explained

Rows ran up and down hill . . . topsoil ran only one way.

it to me. He said I ought not to plant corn on that hill over there, but there wasn't no place else to plant it close enough so's I could take care of it. He said this cotton field here by the house oughta be terraced, too. But I'm tellin' you the truth, the boys and me got just about all we can do to raise what cotton we get, along with the corn and peanuts. And we *got* to raise 'em – corn for the mule, peanuts for the cow. And the kids eat 'em too. And cotton – cotton's our only cash crop! We gotta take care of that. So I guess we just wouldn't have time. I'm not saying conservation wouldn't be a good thing – it might be. I don't know."

Fred Johnson isn't the only one who doesn't know. There are thousands of townspeople and farm people alike, who don't know because they don't understand fully. Many of them just naturally don't care. So they go on plowing and planting up and down hill.

Unfortunately, many of America's most important crops inevitably cause serious erosion by water on sloping land and by wind on dry, loose soil, unless careful preventive measures are used. These crops include cotton and tobacco, and the essential food crops of corn, peanuts and vegetables. Even such fruits as peaches and other stone fruits, and commercially-grown grapes, are included.

These are known as clean-tilled crops. They must

be cultivated constantly during the growing season to keep down weeds, conserve soil moisture, and keep the plants growing and in good condition. This means that the soil, which contains the plant nutrients essential to growth, is kept bare throughout the summer. When the hard rains come it washes away readily. If the slope is rather steep and the rows run up and down hill, like Fred Johnson's corn rows, the field will gully badly. The notorious 50,000 acres of gullies in Stewart County, Georgia, were caused by hillside cultivation without protection.

However, if all these crops, essential to us, endanger the soil, there are other crops, also useful to us, that are good for the land and protect it. These include densely-growing cover crops which spread a thick protective blanket over the earth, and plants which actually enrich the soil. Some do both.

Clover is such a crop, and so are the lespedezas, another group of the legume family. So is kudzu, and so are many grasses, and so are mixtures of grasses and legumes. Some of these are used in rotations and some in winter covers. Lespedezas are good winter covers in the south, and rye is used in the north.

It is the legumes which enrich the soil where they grow. They do it by taking nitrogen from the air and storing it in the earth. As a result, land on which clover or alfalfa or lespedeza has been grown for a year or two will give a much better yield of corn, for example, than a field in which corn follows corn or wheat. This explains why legumes are so widely used in rotations: two years of a suitable legume in a four-year or five-year rotation with non-legumes will step up yields of the intervening crops amazingly, and in addition the grower can get excellent hay crops from the legumes themselves. Not all legumes are entirely beneficial, however: peanuts, beans, and peas are clean-tilled crops that frequently offer only slight physical protection to the soil.

Cover crops are widely used in rotations on strip-cropped fields. In such a field the land is laid out in strips 40 to 100 or more feet wide, preferably on the contour. Alternate strips are planted to the main clean-tilled crop—corn, for instance—and the intervening buffer strips are planted in a cover crop: a legume or a suitable grass, depending upon the region, perhaps, and upon the rotation. Such a field yields two crops each year: one of corn and one of hay.

Under the rotation plan, the same strip ordinarily doesn't grow a clean-tilled crop two years in succession. The rest period permits the corn strips to recover somewhat, and where legumes are used in the buffers, the soil is actually enriched by the nitrogen. Grasses and other non-leguminous winter covers add no nitrogen to the soil, but they do add humus when plowed under, which is highly beneficial.

Sometimes, when the slope is quite gentle, contour cultivation is enough to prevent erosion. On slightly steeper slopes, strip-cropping may be necessary, the buffer strips of close-growing crops serving to catch and hold topsoil and water from clean-tilled strips above. On still steeper slopes, terracing may be required.

A method known as stubble-mulch is used to protect fallow land and clean-tilled fields over winter. Stubble mulch means leaving on the land—or plowing partly under—crop residues, such as cornstalks standing after harvest. Straw is used in the same way.

These are some of the things Fred Johnson—and thousands more—don't know about, or don't understand, or don't care about.

These are the simplest facts about erosion and a few of the means of controlling it. They are, you might say, the merest elementary steps in conservation, which is a much more significant thing than merely cultivating on the contour and growing alfalfa on a field two years out of five.

Considering that it is such a simple term, conservation has been amazingly misunderstood. Some people have the idea that it means a miserly hoarding of all natural wealth for possible use at some vague time in the future. These people have not even grasped the spirit of conservation.

Others assume that it means the plugging of gullies on eroded hillsides. People who think that gully-plugging alone tells the conservation story have seen only one small detail in the whole comprehensive picture.

Conservation is a much greater and more intelligent thing than hoarding; a much more vital and positive thing than stopping gullies.

In reasoned terms, conservation means intelligent utilization of our resources today and their maintenance for the use of our children tomorrow.

In the living, breathing terms in which we of today are accustomed to speak, conservation is the nation's hope for a future of security and happiness. As armaments are our defense against external aggression, so conservation is our defense against national poverty.

As it is the hope of the nation, conservation is also the hope of the millions of men, women, and children who make up the nation. Let your imagination play for a few moments on what conservation could do for Fred Johnson and his wife and eight children, if it were properly applied to their farm.

It would mean, to begin with, putting the farm in good physical shape. The gullies would be stopped with some such prolific perennial legume as kudzu or other adaptable plantings. Diversion ditches might be built around the gully heads to carry away runoff water harmlessly.

The steep hillsides that already have been cleared would be taken out of cultivation, and put in forest or permanent pasture.

The slopes that are not too steep for safe cultivation would be terraced. They would be cultivated on the contour, with the rows running around the hills instead of up and down. In some fields strips of close-growing, soil-holding crops would be alternated with strips of row crops such as corn, cotton, or potatoes.

Johnson would give up cotton, which has been eating the life out of his fields for years, as it has over so much of the South, and get himself a new cash crop, perhaps more than one. Milk, for example. He knows how to feed cows, because the cow he now has shows a pretty good milk production on her diet of peanuts and peanut hay. By putting some of his land now in crops into permanent pasture, he might be able to care for a small herd that would bring him in milk checks which would equal in a month what he now makes from cotton in a year.

A lot of Southern farmers make good money from their peanuts, too. Peanuts are a double crop. An acre will yield anywhere from 30 to 60 bushels of nuts in the shell and a ton to a ton-and-a-half of good hay besides. Johnson could do worse.

And there are those hillsides with fair-to-middling timber stands—mostly small stuff to be sure, but growing and a potential source of real income in a few years from now, if all the trees are not cut to make a new hillside cornfield.

And what would conservation mean to Johnson economically?

It would mean better crop yields on the properly-protected and properly-cultivated land, and therefore more income from crops grown on that land. Practical farm experience, as well as careful research on the principal types of farm land, has shown that wise conservation measures correctly applied on decent land suitable for cultivation do definitely increase crop yields per acre, and generally for the entire farm.

Conservation would mean new sources of income—from peanuts grown commercially, perhaps. Or from milk, for there is a large area that properly managed would make excellent pasture. It would mean money for fertilizer (which he hasn't been able to buy for years) and for other things he needs for the place. Money to pay his debts.

And what would all these things mean to his family?

They would mean decent, warm clothes for everyone, and a roof over their heads that didn't leak. And a coat of paint for the house.

They would mean better food for the family, for any conservation farm plan should include provision for a vegetable garden, fruit and poultry. Consequently, they would mean better health for everyone.

Conservation would mean security, which the Johnsons haven't known for years. It might conceivably mean eventual farm-ownership for Fred Johnson instead of farm-tenancy—at least a long-time lease. It would certainly mean better financial standing, debts paid and credit good once more.

And it would inevitably mean a sharp rise in the Johnsons' self-respect and in their standing in the community. They would be seen at church more frequently because they'd have clothes they weren't ashamed to go in.

And finally, it would mean that when old Fred Johnson's farming days were done he would leave the farm in better shape than he found it, so that the next generation taking over would not find its heritage of natural resources pillaged and ravished.

That is what conservation can mean to one family. Multiply all these things by hundreds of thousands, and you begin to grasp how much conservation really

Strip-cropping and rotations save soil and boost yields.

means to America, its tremendous possibilities, and the new vigor it can inject into the national life.

Multiply by hundreds of thousands such things as health, self-reliance, courage, education, security, and human happiness, and you get a pretty good idea of what conservation means.

CHAPTER IX

TOWN AND COUNTRY WORK TOGETHER

CONSERVATION IS A PUBLIC SERVICE.

It is a public service in the best sense — just as much as state highway maintenance. And there is an aspect of things being accomplished here and now about much of this work. Take the case of McGregor, Iowa, where exploitation on the land was having disastrous effects on farm and town alike.

McGregor is on the Mississippi River and back of the town is a region of good but hilly farm land. The uplands rise as high as 500 feet above the river in not more than two and a half miles. There are several separate small drainage systems in the region about McGregor. All of these drainages converge just above the town, pass through the town by an inadequate floodway, and then empty into the Mississippi River. The area drained by all these streams is only about 2250 acres.

This relatively small watershed embracing a number of drainage systems, and an unusually rapid rise in the slope, presented a complicated problem.

For years the farmers in the McGregor watershed

have been watching their land erode. Every rain storm, even comparatively light rains, carried away thousands of tons of rich topsoil from the hillsides, and cut gullies across the sloping fields. Heavy rains were, of course, much more disastrous.

The cultivated land in the McGregor watershed has lost approximately 60 percent of its topsoil in the last 75 to 100 years.

The story of the McGregor watershed is all too familiar:

Land in cultivation that should not be. Overgrazing in many cases. No steps taken to protect the steep fields and pastures. Good soil running down the corn rows, rushing down the pasture gullies every time it rained. Gradually the amount of land under cultivation was increased, although quite a bit of it should have been left in woodland.

The farmers were concerned, because unless "something was done" *all* their topsoil would eventually go down river.

The people in McGregor didn't like it either. Every rainstorm that washed topsoil off the farms, carried that topsoil down the several drainages to the point where they converged above the town, picking up all sorts of debris on the way, and shoved the whole mess into the town.

Each rain carried silt—which a half hour before was the valuable part of a man's farm—and accumulated debris into the McGregor storm sewer.

Each heavy rainstorm over the watershed became a flood of major proportions. The several converging drainages brought a terrific mass of water down into the town. The storm sewer could not accommodate the runoff and the overflow roared through the streets, damaged highways and railroads, and filled cellars.

When the floods had passed, the people of McGregor were faced with the unpleasant task of cleaning thousands of tons of silt, rock, and debris off the streets and out of their homes, cellars, and yards. Damage to buildings and houses had to be repaired. Roads had to be restored, and railway tracks rebuilt.

This happened not once but many times. Floods like this cost the town of McGregor and its citizens more than $272,000 between 1908 and 1937. Townspeople and farmers alike suffered because of lack of conservation. Finally a committee of farmers and McGregor businessmen got together to try to work out a solution to this costly problem. They brought the matter to the attention of the Soil Conservation Service.

Surveys were made and a plan involving a soil and water conservation program was worked out. The problem, of course, was twofold: to stop erosion, with

Top: "Sick land" . . . a gully on an Iowa farm.

Bottom: The same gully, healed with black locust.

its attendant water loss, on the upland farms of the watershed; and to stop or reduce flood damage in the town of McGregor.

The proper use of the land was a big factor in the problem as it always is. The surveys showed that 30 percent of the area was in pasture, 32 percent under cultivation, and 30 percent in woodland. The balance was urban area. Practically all of the pasture land was overgrazed, and it was found that, in many cases, slopes of as much as 25 percent were planted to row crops, such as corn, which offered no protection to the topsoil. Erosion was bad over much of the watershed, and getting worse.

Thirty-two of the 40 farmers in the area participated in the conservation plan, and as a result land under cultivation was decreased from 32 percent to 25 percent. The area of permanent pasture and protected woodland has been increased accordingly.

The cooperating farmers put into use such conservation measures as terracing, contour tillage, and strip-cropping, crop rotation, pasture furrows, and diversion ditches. Altogether, more than 25 different conservation measures were used to stabilize the various kinds of land within the drainage basin. These, by holding back the rapid water runoff during storms, accomplished three important things: they helped keep the topsoil where it belonged—on the farm; they also kept on the land some of the water for dry-weather crop use and to build up the underground water supply; and by retarding the runoff of rainwater they helped reduce the flood menace to McGregor.

In addition to these measures on the farms themselves, three earthen retention dams were constructed with concrete spillways, and with adequate storage basin areas, serving a total combined drainage area of 900 acres. These dams hold back the runoff that now comes down from the watershed. The spillways release only as much water as the McGregor storm water channelway can safely handle. Screens above the spillways keep debris out of the storm sewers.

Before the work was quite completed, a five-inch rain fell in twelve hours over the watershed. There was little or no erosion on the farms of the 32 farmers who had cooperated by adopting conservation measures. Erosion on cornfields without control ranged from moderate to severe.

Down in McGregor, not only was there no flood, but the storm sewers were only three-fourths full.

Outside the project area, county authorities reported $50,000 damage to highways, and railroad companies announced $10,000 damage to their rights-of-way, as results of the storm.

This conservation program, planned to help all the people, does the job. It is conserving valuable soil and soil moisture; it has controlled the costly floods in McGregor.

The story of McGregor is a good example of the wide scope that conservation work may have, and shows that it is not only essential but entirely possible to husband all the nation's resources.

CHAPTER X

SCIENCE BLAZES THE TRAIL

IT TOOK NATURE UNDETERMINABLE THOUSANDS OF years to bring the earth to the state in which mankind has known it.

In the United States the white man, by uneconomic and unscientific use of natural resources has undone in three centuries—and mostly in one century—a great deal of the work that nature had accomplished.

Only by hard work, scientifically directed, can we repair the damage in time.

The problems of redemption of the ravished land, rehabilitation of thousands of farm families, stabilization of productive topsoil, reestablishment of economic balance, the development of farm, range, and other programs for conservation and wise use of soil, water, and all our other resources demand the services of many kinds of scientists.

Before any project great or small is undertaken two things are essential: a thorough understanding of existing conditions, their causes and trends; and suitable methods and materials for carrying out the project.

A highway engineer would not even bid for a contract to build a road across the country until the route had been carefully surveyed, the character and amount of rock and clay to be excavated computed, and the availability of building materials determined. Nor would a contractor undertake to build a house without a plan based on the requirements of the client.

The planning and carrying out of a complete conservation program is no less complicated than planning and building a road or a house. It is much *more* complicated.

We have noted how many factors there are to be considered in conservation program planning—even in straight erosion control. Let's take the case of the Fred Johnson family again. There are plenty of factors there to consider.

Fundamental, of course, is the physical factor. Of what kind of land is the Johnson place made up? How much of it should be retired from cultivation and grazing? How much of it may continue in cultivation with somewhat complex and intensive control practices? How much with only one or two special control measures? Is there any that is non-erodible—that it would be safe to cultivate without protection and without danger of erosion?

The first step in setting up a conservation farm program for Fred Johnson would be to determine the answers to these questions, in considerable detail. This is where the first group of scientists comes in—soil scientists, surveyors, and land technologists—and they make a study known as a "land use capability survey." Surveys of this type have been completed on about 120 million acres of land in the United States, and are under way on another 306 million. They are needed on nearly a billion acres in all.

The scientists who make these surveys are not armchair scientists. They go out on the land to study it. They study the kinds of soil, the drainage, the degree and direction of slope; the condition of the land; and its use, as for pasture, woodland, or cultivation.

The ultimate result of this detailed or intensive survey is a map, keyed with various colors and patterns which show the slope of various parts of the area and the use that is being made of all the parts.

This is something Fred Johnson not only can understand—he can see for himself. He can take the map and go out over his farm and stand in a field and compare what the map shows with what his eyes see.

He can go to the steep eroded cornfield on the hillside, and find it on the map.

"Here it is," Johnson says to himself. "Just across that branch from the barn. And it's colored blue. Let's see what that means."

Scientific study is the basis of conservation.

He looks at the color key at the bottom of the map:

"Blue! Class IV land. Not suitable for continuous cultivation."

Fred refers again to the map of the field where he is standing and finds the blue patch marked 48C18. He turns to tables on the back of the map to interpret these symbols.

There he finds that "48" means that the land in that field is damaged by severe sheet erosion and frequent gullies. Startled, he glances across the field and finds it true.

The "C," he next learns, means that the field has a slope of between 25 and 35 per cent, too steep for clean cultivation and suitable only for close-growing crops or trees. And he has to admit to himself that it *is* pretty steep. The "18" means simply that the field is poorly drained, sloping land, in this case a type of silt loam.

All over the farm Fred Johnson can go, color map in hand, and see for himself. He finds a lot of land on the map marked in blue—that's steep land.

He sees quite a bit marked in salmon color: Class V land, not suitable for cultivation. "Not even hay, I guess," he mutters.

There is a considerable amount printed in pink. He looks that up and finds that pink means Class III land, suitable for cultivation with complex or intensive practices. And a few fields marked in yellow, which means Class II, suitable for cultivation with simple practices. His eye moves over to the only other square in the color key—green.

"Wonder have I got any green land?" he says. "Yep, there's two patches."

He looks at the key again. Green means Class I land, suitable for cultivation without special practices: nearly level and not subject to erosion—not even in need of ditching and no stones to pick off.

The map shows these two fields to be at the far end of the farm from the house, and not very large, but Johnson is pleased to find any land at all that doesn't need a lot of extra work.

As he continues to study the map he becomes aware of the relation between the use of the land and soil erosion. He stands in the steep cornfield and sees the gullies, but the map puts it down on paper for him and makes the connection clearer. He starts to check the map further. Here's another piece of "blue land"—slope 25 to 35 percent—yet the erosion, according to the symbol, is only slight in that area. Why? The gray pattern over the area tells why: it is in woodland.

With a start Johnson realizes that this gray-patterned blue patch on the map is the "patch over yonder on that hill" that he planned to clear during the coming winter and put in corn next spring.

The connection between land abuse and soil erosion, and the whole concept of conservation are suddenly clarified.

These things are being clarified for thousands of farmers throughout the United States as they study these land use capability maps. And always they demand: "What shall we do about it?"

But Fred Johnson cannot have his answer quite yet. So far only the physical survey has been completed, and this simply establishes the physical or soil conditions and limitations within which a sound conservation farm plan must be worked out.

There are, as we know only too well, other factors that the scientists have to consider: the human factors and the economic factors. Any steps to repair damages to the land and to change the use of land must necessarily be affected and modified by the human and economic factors, which are of course very closely interrelated.

Now a lot of other information must be gathered: how many in the Johnson family, their ages, sexes, their health, and—to be quite practical about it—how many of them are able to help with the farm work? This is important in a family like the Johnsons who are likely to have more muscle than money to expend on improvements.

We need to know how much cash Fred Johnson takes in each year, and how much money he owes, what his taxes are, how much it would cost to fix the roof so it wouldn't leak.

We need to know where he trades, and where his closest markets for farm produce are and what farm produce finds readiest sale there at decent prices.

Gathering all this information is the work of another group of specialists: sociologists, economists, marketing experts, statisticians. This is the kind of survey that correlates Fred Johnson's personal affairs with his farming affairs, and balances income and need against the capacity and capability of the farm.

Without these various surveys it is next to impossible to plan intelligently the essential steps to conserve our soil and plant resources and to conserve rainfall for plant use.

On the other hand, with this information available, flexible conservation programs and farm plans can be developed which will enable us to meet all production

A land of ungullied fields, comfortable homes, security and freedom.

demands on the land without injury to the soil, without waste of any natural resources.

The data provided by these surveys is used by the agronomists, engineers, and other technologists in working out the complete "farm plan"—Fred Johnson's new "design for farming."

CHAPTER XI

NEW DESIGN FOR FARMING

HIS FARM PLAN IS SOMETHING EACH CONSERVATION farmer awaits with a great deal of curiosity, a certain amount of restrained eagerness, and perhaps some degree of ill-disguised apprehension.

Of one thing he feels sure—and usually he is quite correct—the plan is going to make considerable difference in his farming methods. No more doing it the way his father and grandfather did. That's what's the matter with the old place now. Already, too many years—and too much soil—have been lost.

Well, the plan does make a difference. Take Fred Johnson's place. No more corn and cotton on those steep hillsides. There are some Class II and Class III areas that can be used, and those two patches of green on the map would be good for either cotton or corn.

Contour cultivation will take care of most of the Class II fields with perhaps strip cropping in some of them. And terraces can help make some of the Class III land available for safe cultivation.

A few patches may be used for pasture but not cultivation, and a lot of this land should be in woodland. In fact, if some areas are not planted to trees pretty quick there'll be nothing left but the rocky skeletons of what were once fertile, wooded hills.

Into the carrying out of the plan goes a lot more technical or scientific assistance.

The types of terraces best suited to the various slopes and soils on the Johnson place have not been worked out on paper by office experts, but on the earth itself.

Systems for utilizing crop residues as mulches to protect the soil have been determined by farmer experience and by research. So have the types of grasses best suited for sodding channels or waterways for carrying off runoff water. So have the grasses best adapted to anchoring soil against wind erosion where that is a problem. So have been the various mechanical measures taken to halt erosion.

Physiographers and conservation specialists have studied the earth itself, to ascertain what relation its own movements, such as earth-flow or soil-creep, have to land decline.

Climatologists have studied rainfall and snowfall and evaporation and checked these against data on erosion and runoff, to help determine finally what may be done to *offset* the action of that force which cannot be controlled by man—the weather.

Hydrologists have studied the behavior of water through every phase of the hydrologic cycle, but particularly with reference to the movement of water over and into the earth: runoff and infiltration or water intake on various kinds of soil, and the varying abilities of different types of vegetation to retard runoff or increase rainfall intake.

One of the interesting research projects carried out by the hydrologists was a study of the effect of the size and velocity of raindrops on erosion and infiltration. Small drops and gentle rains allowed more infiltration into the soil, but as the drops increased in size and violence, infiltration dropped and erosion increased as much as 1200 percent.

Offhand, it might appear that this particular piece of research yielded mildly interesting information which is, however, of little practical value since there is no way to regulate the size or speed of raindrops.

Actually, this information proved to be of tremendous value. The hydrologists went further in their experiments and found, through trying different types of vegetation on the earth, that the terminal velocity of the raindrops—velocity at the instant of impact which is what counts—is controlled not by the distance of fall but by the nature of the growing crop or the amount of crop stubble or vegetative material over the field on which it falls.

Other scientists are examining silt loads—the soil

A conservation farm map clarifies the farmer's problems.

materials carried in suspension by running water—and silt deposits in streams and reservoirs. These sedimentation studies have been useful in establishing the relationship between erosion and floods. They have shown the extent of damage done to reservoirs and streams by being filled gradually with soil material washed down from farmlands in the watershed. They have shown the effects of erosion on aquatic wildlife. These matters are of direct concern, certainly, to townspeople as well as farmers, since wildlife, navigable streams and water-supply reservoirs are important to everyone.

Scientific studies have been made and are being made of various phases of drainage, and of irrigation in the arid regions of the west, too.

These are typical of the many types of research projects that are assisting in the development of the mechanical control measures that are recommended for Fred Johnson's farm. But what about his cash crop? Not sufficient suitable acreage to make a cotton crop big enough to amount to much. Still, a man's got to have a cash crop.

And that's where another group of research scientists—the hillculturists—is called in. Hillculture is exactly what the word indicates—a type of farming particularly adapted to hillsides, that will yield income for the farmer and, at the same time, conserve soil and plant resources.

Hillculture is an intriguing word. It conjures up pictures of hillsides with slopes ranging from gentle to precipitous, not eroded and gashed with raw, red gullies, but abundantly wooded with trees and undergrowth, all of which mean money to the farmer, now and later.

If a man sets his mind to it, he can grow a lot of things on a hillside—a lot of things that will make money for him, and yield something else, too—a deep inner satisfaction not at having taken all he could wrest from the land by force, but from having used his land thoughtfully and having left the soil unharmed for his son and his grandson, perhaps, to use years later.

Hillside woodlands, properly cared for, can produce valuable timber, varying of course with latitude, altitude, soil, and climate.

They can produce alone or as undergrowth in a woodland, fruiting or ornamental shrubbery. There are people who make money from holly grown in their woodlots. Hillsides may make excellent spots for fruit orchards, and for groves of nut trees.

Hillculture farming offers thousands of farmers not only economic hope but the prospect of delightful work and life, because of the variety of opportunities it presents. There are a lot of farmers with hill land who will find it the answer.

Fred Johnson is one of these, for this farm of his was apparently made for hillculture. So the hillculturists make recommendations to him based on extensive research on farms, in the laboratory, in the greenhouse, and at experiment stations. Their work is aided by the men who seek out additional varieties of plants to try. These plant scientists are constantly on the hunt for hitherto untried trees, shrubs, herbs, and grasses that will hold soil a little better perhaps than those already in use, and will yield the grower just as much income or perhaps a little more.

So do the scientists keep everlastingly on, trying to find better solutions to the farmers' problems—including erosion and its attendant evils.

CHAPTER XII

FROM EXPLOITATION TO CONSERVATION

CONSERVATION OF SOIL AND WATER IS NOT A NEW THING. It has been practiced here and there in America since colonial days. Erosion became a bothersome farm problem in North America as far back as the seventeenth century, and there were a few thoughtful men even in those days who understood its danger.

In 1685, William Byrd of Virginia wrote of a heavy rainstorm that carried away the growing tobacco crop and "all of the top of the manured land"—evidently a case of serious sheet erosion.

Then came Jared Eliot, clergyman and physician of Connecticut, who studied erosion on his neighbors' farms as he went about his parochial and professional calls. He studied causes and experimented with remedies zealously, and evolved theories on erosion control, sedimentation and drainage, and soil-building, which were widely used long after his death.

Thomas Jefferson preached and practiced what he called "horizontal plowing"—the contour cultivation of today—down in Albemarle County, Virginia, to stop the rich topsoil from running off into the streams.

Samuel Deane of Maine, preacher and farmer, experimented with crop rotations, contour cultivation, and means of combatting wind erosion. Then Solomon Drown (1753-1834), farmer, surgeon and college professor of Rhode Island, studied wind-erosion control by cover crops, and urged rotations which he called "alternate husbandry." In approximately the same period John Taylor of Virginia was denouncing the "ruinous evil" of erosion, and urged control by "horizontal plowing."

During the early years of the nineteenth century John Lorain of Pennsylvania wrote of erosion as "an insatiable monster" and, among other things, urged grasses as erosion-control crops. There were others, too, who understood what was happening to the land, and tried to impress upon farmers the importance of conservation measures. Sometimes they were successful in a small way: terracing of sloping fields was practiced to some extent in South Carolina in the 1830's.

But for the most part these men were "as voices crying in the wilderness," and as agriculture pushed westward out of hearing of the warnings, they lost what effectiveness they had.

It was considerably more than a half-century before the government officially recognized erosion. About four decades ago the Department of Agriculture undertook a series of soil surveys. Some of these early land studies were made in the South, such as those in Fairfield County, South Carolina; Stuart County, Georgia; and Lauderdale County, Mississippi. In some of these, the impoverishing and destroying effects of erosion were pointed out and, to some extent, measured.

Actual measurement of soil and water losses from land used for different types of crops began in a small way in Missouri in 1917, and later in Texas and North Carolina. And foresters had made a few measurements. But these projects barely touched the problem. As a nation we were not yet ready to launch an "all-out" attack on erosion.

It was not until the spring of 1929 that intensive governmental study of soil erosion was begun. At that time the first erosion-control experiment station was established at Guthrie, Oklahoma. Other stations were started within a few months in Missouri, Iowa, Texas, and North Carolina. These were made possible by an amendment to the Agricultural Appropriations Bill, introduced by Congressman James Paul Buchanan of Texas. The Buchanan Amendment was the real turning point from soil exploitation to soil conservation. Eventually ten stations similar to the one at Guthrie were set up by the Department of Agriculture in regions where erosion was most severe.

Gullies big enough to drop a house in.

By 1933 soil erosion was taking on many of the aspects of a national emergency. The growing seriousness of the problem made action imperative and the country got action!

In September of that year the Soil Erosion Service was established in the Department of the Interior to demonstrate the practical possibilities of erosion control. This Service immediately began to set up erosion-control demonstration projects in problem areas.

In 1935 this Service was transferred to the Department of Agriculture, and by Congressional action the name was changed to Soil Conservation Service. Since then this bureau has been the spearhead of the soil conservation movement throughout the United States. Many other agencies have taken part, approaching the problem from many different sides, but, because of its specific legislative charter, the Soil Conservation Service has had a more direct and definite role than any other agency.

Once more, pioneers—soil scientists, biologists, hydrologists, agronomists and others—set out across the land, following the trails of devastation left by the exploiters.

This new movement was not as dramatic, not as spectacular as the march of the exploiters, but, when historians a hundred or two hundred years from now review these times, it will stand out as one of the significant movements in the story of the nation.

There was little of the swashbuckling or romantic about these men as they moved over America. They were hard-working rather than colorful. They had ahead of them a gigantic task. On their ability and sincerity rested a tremendous responsibility, for only the successful performance of the job could insure the nation's future self-sufficiency.

The job of these new pioneers was not as simple as that of the men who had passed that way a century and more before. It was not as simple as cutting down trees and plowing up grass.

There were surveys to be made to determine how much land had been impoverished and the degree of damage; and research into methods of restoring the soil; a solution to be devised for the problem of the people on the ruined land.

These things were done—not by magic, but by hard work. Not overnight, but through weeks and months and years of unremitting effort, often against the terrific odds of inertia, skepticism, and sometimes downright opposition.

They are still being done today, for applying conservation to an area the size of the United States is no flash proposition—it is a long-time job.

Naturally, the new movement was not received with open arms from the outset. Some farmers were somewhat dubious or distrustful at first. This was, as they saw it, a new kind of agricultural endeavor involving something of the experimental.

The erosion-control demonstration projects, however, showed the farmers of America that control of erosion was not only possible, but practicable.

They proved it—over a period of time, with a lot of work. Even black-locust seedlings do not become twenty-foot trees overnight. And it takes work to contour fields, build terraces, and construct diversion ditches. It takes work, and it takes a lot of study and planning beforehand.

Much of the early effort of these scientists led them into new problems. Many other factors than slope of the land influenced conditions and results, they found.

They found that the way land is used is a fundamental factor. That led to studies in land utilization.

They verified what they had suspected—that erosion is closely tied up with floods. Even in arid sections they found the water problem not only one of rainfall scarcity but also at times a problem of destructive "flash" floods, which carried away the precious water.

They discovered that some crops held soil in place better than others, and this led to the inevitable conclusion that altering the use of land sometimes was the only solution that promised success—a conclusion that had terrific sociological as well as economic significance. They discovered the intricate interrelationship of all these and many other factors.

They quickly came to realize that the laws of nature are inexorable; that they cannot be repealed or amended no matter how much they may irk mankind. And from all these new understandings came two clear realizations:

Soil Conservation means more than stopping erosion on hillsides. It means conservation of people as well as conservation of resources of the land. And you cannot consider either without considering the other.

Conservation cannot be accomplished by a few, but must be accomplished by the whole people.

Naturally, since most of the land on which conservation methods are needed is land used for agriculture or related activities, the farmers of America are foremost in the fight to save the soil.

They have organized themselves into units to carry on the fight together.

These units are the Soil Conservation Districts—and there are more than 700 of them in the fight throughout the United States.

A hill-and-valley farm doesn't *have* to be wasted by erosion.

CHAPTER XIII

DEMOCRACY ON THE LAND

DRIVE ALONG A WINDING DIRT ROAD BESIDE A GURGLING stream in the Arkansas Ozarks, between woods of oak, ash, sycamore, sassafras, hickory, and short-leaf pine, laced with dogwood, edged with sumac, red bud, and wild rose—

Go out a sandy Georgia road between the tall ranks of long-leaf pine, past once-raw gullies now clothed in kudzu—

Out a Wisconsin "hard road" between green pastures, grazed by sleek dairy cattle, or out dust-blown trails across the plains where the tumbleweed rolls before the ceaseless wind—

There, in all those places and in many others you will find the Soil Conservation District.

From one of them came the following:

"The cash registers tinkle more frequently in our business firms, bank deposits of farmers have increased, and the Federal Land Bank has no delinquent loans in any of the three associations operating in the Tri-River District. The once-almost-extinct rural community centers are being restored as land tenure and ownership become secure through proper land use, thereby stabilizing and improving not only the soil but the livelihood of the people.

"It is not for the sake of the soil alone that we attempt to keep our district alive to the fundamentals of good farming practices, but for the maintenance of the farm families who take their living from this soil with their own hands. We are firm in our belief in the statement of President Franklin D. Roosevelt that '*the soil is truly our first line of national defense,*' and our strength for the holding of this line consequently becomes greater as new cooperators join our ranks."

The foregoing is quoted from a statement by the Board of Supervisors of the Tri-River Soil Conservation District in Arkansas. It is an expression of courage and practical optimism by a group of realistic men, men who still can keep their eyes fixed on ideals while facing reality, for in this same statement they declare:

"To say that our program of erosion control is completely established after only two years would be an exaggeration, but we *are* safe in saying that our soil is being rapidly tied down by permanent grass, legumes, crop rotations, forestry improvement, and many other phases of the movement which we like to call the conservation of the American way of life."

It is extremely significant that this statement was conceived, written, and issued by a group of farmers—men who "*take their living from this soil with their own hands.*"

For all that farmers are individualists, there is a strong unanimity of thought among them on important issues, and this statement from the Arkansas Tri-River District may be accepted as a statement from the farmers of America.

Such statements are most encouraging because they indicate recognition not only of the importance of the conservation program, but also the importance of the human being and the determination of the American people to stand together in democratic unity to protect the nation's soil resources for the sake of the people.

Soil Conservation Districts are, of course, essentially democratic mechanisms. They are the farmers' own governmental units—of, for, and by farmers. They are *not*, as some people suppose, units of the Soil Conservation Service. There is no administrative or fiscal connection between them and the Service.

Soil Conservation Districts are organized and operated by farmers, in states where enabling legislation has been adopted, to deal with erosion and related problems that already existing agencies of government, local, state or federal, have not been able or authorized to deal with.

Under these enabling laws, the Soil Conservation

Districts have authority to carry out soil conservation measures on any land within the district, either public or private, with the voluntary cooperation of the owner or user of the land.

Districts may act as land-management agencies and, as such, acquire lands by purchase or lease and administer those lands and control their use in any way that will best benefit the district as a whole.

The districts are run by their members; the affairs of the districts are administered by a board of supervisors or directors elected from among the farmer-members.

When a group of farmers in an area decide that their efforts to conserve their soil resources would be more effective if they worked together on the problem, they can take the first step toward a district by circulating a petition, calling for a referendum on the formation of a district. When the necessary signatures are available, the referendum is held in accordance with the State act.

In most states, after the district organization is completed, the directors or supervisors sign a Memorandum of Understanding with the Secretary of Agriculture, providing for assistance by the Department to the district.

The first business undertaken in most districts is the

The farmers work out plans together.

preparation of a district conservation program and work plan with assistance of Soil Conservation Service field technicians when requested. Many of the districts also work closely with other federal and state agencies. Individual farmers then enter into cooperative agreements with the districts.

Working out of the individual farm plans is one of the most significant and important phases of the whole procedure. Meetings of groups of farmers are held to discuss farm plans, at which soil and water conservation technicians are asked to be present. Aerial photographs sometimes are provided of the farms these men operate, and each farmer then works out a conservation plan for his place, based on what he has learned through reading, personal experience, talks, motion pictures, and other educational media.

The farmers then study, criticize, and discuss each others' plans, with help from the technicians when necessary. These discussions have been extremely valuable. They have clarified the men's own ideas, the men have been able to help one another, and they have developed *that unity of thought and action which makes any community effort so effective.*

As they work out the plans together, so the farmers learn the techniques together, from the way to use a hand level in laying out contours, to how to build terraces. And when it comes to carrying out the work plans, they often work together.

In many districts the farmers themselves do most of the work. That is an important point about the district plan. The individual farmer under the district plan has to put much of his own time, muscle, and material into the work. And it is a trait of human nature that people value most that which costs them most in money or effort. In some districts part of the actual labor may be furnished. In certain cases CCC camp enrollees have supplied part of the labor. Some districts sponsor work projects to aid with the labor. *Every stroke of labor performed in the safeguarding of the communities' and the nation's most basic natural resource is public labor because it contributes to public welfare.*

In some cases, the Soil Conservation Service lends equipment, such as terracers, tractors, and graders, to district officials, since most of these districts have very limited or no operating funds. In some other instances county or state government units have made money grants to districts. This is welcome aid, because in most states, Soil Conservation Districts do not have authority to levy taxes or to make charges for work done or for facilities used.

Naturally, since *districts are autonomous subdivisions of local government*, many of the details of procedure will vary from state to state, but in the main they conform to the foregoing.

The districts' businesslike way of going about things has made a favorable impression on both rural and urban people living in or near the districts. Business men in the towns—merchants, bankers, editors, teachers, and others—are particularly interested because they have found that everything that helps farmers helps the entire community as well.

In many places, tours of districts have been arranged for the townspeople in order to enable them to see, at first hand, what is being done to save the soil. Out in Arkansas, in the Magazine District, one of the first of these tours was staged by the editor of a newspaper at Booneville, cooperating with the Booneville Chamber of Commerce. They sent six bus loads of visitors, expenses paid, to look at the new methods of soil saving as practiced on the Poteau Valley Soil and Water Conservation Demonstration Project, thirty miles away. This public-spirited step bore fruit shortly after in the formation of the Magazine District.

The tour idea took hold with the growing districts, for here was something for people to see. Good news is rarely as sensational as bad news, but here was something almost as dramatic as the raw, ugly gullies which had scarred the hillsides, and people flocked to see it. Such tours—short but forceful courses in local history—have been in many states the districts' answer to the doubters—an answer which demonstrates the alertness of these farmer organizations.

The first state soil conservation district law was adopted in 1937. In March, 1942, there were more than 700 districts in operation in thirty-nine states, representing a membership of more than a million-and-a-half farm families and a total acreage of over 413 million. Since the establishment of these districts, many of them have been increased in size by petition of neighboring farmers.

The only states which do not have districts laws are Connecticut, Massachusetts, Missouri, New Hampshire, and Rhode Island, but this list is shrinking. The district idea has not stopped spreading. Within the last year Wyoming, Maine, Arizona, Delaware, and Ohio have adopted such laws.

Thus is spreading throughout the nation the new democracy of farmers who provide the food and fiber for the nation, who "take their living from the soil with their own hands" and are working for "conservation of the American way of living."

CHAPTER XIV

ACHIEVEMENTS

BUILD A DIRT ROAD EIGHT TIMES AROUND THE EARTH AT the equator—200,000 miles of it—and you'd have a good idea of the amount of erosion-control terraces built on United States farms under Soil Conservation Service technical supervision.

But you wouldn't have a complete picture of the progress made along all lines by the national conservation program. The terraces, important though they are, are only a detail in the whole picture.

Many of the most outstanding achievements in conservation which the Service has chalked up on its records cannot be measured in terms of miles or of acres. Many of them, in fact, cannot be measured at all. These are the gains in human happiness, in hope, in optimism, in self-respect, in national security.

It is in its effect on the lives of human beings that conservation is brought to the finest focus. Let an actual case from government records demonstrate this. The case is that of the Harrisons, a farm family living in that sprawling, everchanging area known as the "Dust Bowl."

It was April in this land of ceaseless wind and dust.

The dust had been worse than usual that year and although it was now late in the spring the farmer and his son had been unable to get any wheat in. And even if they had, it wouldn't have grown; it hadn't rained for so long that the earth was dry as powder, so the topsoil blew away. And even if the wheat could come up, chances are it would be blown out by the ruthless wind.

Family after family, the people in the township abandoned their blowing farms. They loaded all of the household and personal belongings possible on the family car or truck and started out to look for a place where "a man's farm would stay put and he could grow a crop." The Harrisons had thus lost about all their neighbors. Only one other family remained in that neighborhood—the Millers, six miles away.

One day in April Mr. Harrison's son and his wife and two children drove to the county seat, as much to get away from the maddening monotony of wind and dust and inactivity as for any other reason. They had no money to spend.

They returned shortly after noon in the midst of a terrific dust storm.

"The Millers are pulling out this afternoon," said the younger Harrison grimly. "Met John in town and he told me."

"There go our last neighbors," his father replied, and slowly added: "Maybe that's the only thing to do—get out!"

"No, Dad. Let's wait. Here's some more news. There's a meeting in town tonight. Fellows from the Department of Agriculture at Washington and the Agricultural College are going to talk about putting in crops. I figure we'd better go."

"Well, if there's any way to get a crop in that'll do any good, I want to know about it. Yes, we'll go!"

The Harrisons, father and son, went to the meeting. After the meeting they came back home more hopeful than they had been for months. At the meeting they had heard Department of Agriculture soil technicians discussing methods of halting wind erosion and beating the drought.

"And they're coming out to the place tomorrow to tell us what we can do about it, or whether we'd better just give up and clear out too," Mr. Harrison concluded his recital to the family.

The government technicians did not tell the Harrisons they'd "better give up and clear out." They urged them to stay, and showed them how they could tie down their blowing and washing soil and make it produce crops again.

The first thing the Harrisons did, at the suggestion of

the Soil Conservation Service technicians, was to build terraces in their fields.

"I thought people used terraces on hilly land to keep rain from washing the topsoil down," observed Mr. Harrison.

"That's right," one of the technicians told him. "You've got enough slope here for topsoil to wash down—when it rains," he added with a grin. "You're getting sheet erosion here every rain that falls. These terraces will stop that and they'll also help to hold the water on the land, instead of letting it run off the way it's been doing. You say it's been dry here for months, and tests certainly don't show much moisture in the soil. These terraces'll hold water back long enough so it can soak into the ground."

The next month—May—the Harrisons plowed their terraced fields. Not up and down, of course, as they had in the past, but following the terraces around the contours which the Service men had showed them how to lay out.

Finally, acting upon suggestions of the conservationists, the Harrisons seeded the new fields to crops that would be likely to succeed under the extremely dry soil conditions of that year and that would contribute something to the enrichment of the soil.

Rains were even lighter than usual that spring, but

Cotton-farming along new lines in Dixie.

what rain there was stayed where it fell—soaked into the ground—and that summer, for the first time in four years, the Harrisons looked out across green fields instead of dust-brown wastes. They had a fair harvest that year, and at harvest time they left the roots in the ground and the stalks standing—a variety of the "stubble mulch" practice.

The stubble material kept the land from being blown by the winds of fall, winter, and early spring. When plowing time came next year, the protected soil was all there and in better condition than it had been. There was a better harvest that year than the year before.

By the third year, enough moisture and vitality had been restored to the Harrisons' land to grow wheat again, and once more they found good years on the farm. They saw their fields green again and their cattle fat once more. Their self-respect grew—no longer were they beaten people, about ready to "clear out." As their crops improved their income grew, their living standards improved, and they knew a happiness they had not known for years.

Furthermore, adoption of the conservation measures saved for the nation a good farm that might otherwise have been left to blow away and become a desert. And every acre of good land preserved adds to the national security.

These are the achievements of conservation that cannot be measured in miles or acres or any other units.

These are the things that all engaged in the conservation movement are really working for, when you come right down to it. The miles of terraces, the acres of contour tillage, the number of trees planted – these are only the physical symbols of the real achievements of the conservation program.

And the Harrisons are symbols of thousands of other farm families. There are many other cases: in the South, the East, the North-Central regions, the Southern Great Plains, the West Coast, the Southwest, the Mississippi Valley – cases of families who are "better off" after adopting conservation methods, as well as families who still need conservation badly.

What conservation could do for Fred Johnson's hill farm, what it did for the Harrisons in the "Dust Bowl," it has done and can do for people all over America.

It has done more than that! It has stabilized the people *on* the land as well as the land itself. Farmers do not abandon farms that are producing and increasing in value. Farms operated under conservation programs are worth more after the programs are put into effect than they were before.

Conservation farms produce bigger crop yields per acre and bigger farm incomes naturally follow, other circumstances being equal, which means better living for the people on the farm. A farm conservation program which may in many cases include wise changes in land use, likewise may open up new sources of farm income.

Worn-out lands are retired from cultivation under conservation programs, and this means that no longer do beaten people struggle to wrest a scanty livelihood from wretched soil.

With the productiveness of much of the country's grazing land at a low state, new pasture becomes of great economic importance. Much of the devastated cropland which has been retired from cultivation is being converted into pasture—and every acre of this becomes an asset instead of a liability.

Our forests have been sharply reduced in area and value by exploitation—overcutting. Many thousands of acres of retired land have been planted to trees, and these areas now are developing, as the trees grow, into valuable timber sources for the nation's use in the future. More than 544,000 acres have been planted to trees and shrubs, requiring 635,000,000 seedlings.

The uncountable value of such work as this—a value that would make its cost seem a matter of pennies if a figure could be placed on it—may be better realized when it is understood exactly what reforestation does.

It utilizes land that cannot produce other crops; it protects the land from erosion; it contributes to reduction of the hazards of floods and silting; it helps guarantee the nation a continuance of its timber supply, and offers the farm a new potential source of income. These things are important inasmuch as nearly one-third of America's forest land is on farms. Where American farms now supply one-eighth of the nation's wood needs, they could supply a third if the farm woodlands were all properly maintained by a good conservation program. The importance of a good supply of lumber can hardly be exaggerated.

There is another phase of the conservation program that offers real value to the nation. This is the wildlife conservation work that is being done.

The wildlife of a country is as much a national resource as timber, and conservation of the soil, the water, and vegetation of all types almost inevitably results in conservation of wildlife of all kinds. The two things are pretty nearly inseparable.

The fact is simply that ample vegetation of types needed to prevent erosion increases wildlife by providing better cover and food supplies. Let's take a simple illustration.

Fish cannot live in water that is filled with silt—soil particles in suspension—nor in streams whose beds have

Contour cultivation . . . strip-cropping . . . on 2,000,000 acres.

been covered with deposits of eroded soil. Mud, if present in great quantities in suspension in water, may clog a fish's gills. Mud on the stream bed buries the minute crustaceans and the aquatic plants on the bottom which are sources of the fish's food. Consequently fish die out and disappear.

If we prevent erosion from removing soil from the farms to the streams, and allow the streams to run clear, that gives the fish a chance; and given a chance, other conditions being favorable, they multiply.

Game birds and game animals likewise do best and multiply most rapidly under conditions of vegetation which provide them the most protective cover, the most shelter in winter, and the best food supply. Thus quail are not found in open fields which are cleared right up to the fences on all sides—free of weeds and brush and "clean as a whistle."

Here is a case from one of the Middle Western states. Two comparable and almost adjoining farm sites were chosen. One site, scarred by erosion, was about as "clean" as it was possible for man to make it. There were few weeds, brambles or brush—little cover—on the field or around the borders.

On the other site erosion-control measures had been put into effect. Small gullies had been planted, and dense brush had been established along fence rows with tall grass in the space intervening between the brush and the tilled field. Plenty of cover here, and food too, for the shrubbery and grass had been selected with those things in mind.

Surveys showed nearly 100 percent more wildlife in the conservation-treated field than in the barren field!

These things are not the whole sum of conservation – they are symbols of the progress being made on 1500 projects of all kinds in the United States, Puerto Rico, and the Hawaiian Islands, involving a total area of more than 600,000,000 acres. That's more than 31 percent of the total area of the United States, Hawaii and Puerto Rico.

Here are some of the specific measures that have been established on many critical portions of those 600 million acres. The 200,000 miles of terraces built by farmers with help of Soil Conservation Service technicians, protect 2,900,000 acres of cultivated farmland against erosion.

Contour cultivation has been put into effect on two million acres, and so has strip-cropping.

More than 3400 farm families in the arid regions, with holdings of more than three million acres of land, have been aided under the small water facilities program, to build farm pools, stock ponds, dams and similar facilities to aid their farm operations and conserve both their soil and water resources. Land utilized in projects of these kinds is generally unfit for crop production of any kind, but by such use as this, it becomes productive land from an economic standpoint.

These facts and figures are merely indicative of progress. There is a tremendous amount yet to be done, but we are making headway more satisfactorily all the time. Many groups are aiding the farmers in their fight to preserve the soil. The story would be incomplete if it didn't note, in addition to work of the Soil Conservation Service, the contributions of the Farm Security Administration, the Forest Service, the Bureau of Agricultural Economics, the Agricultural Adjustment Agency, and the Extension Service, all of which are giving valuable assistance to the conservation movement. There are likewise the various State Extension Services, and the agricultural experiment stations and agricultural colleges which have made important contributions. These are powerful factors.

But most powerful of all is the demonstrated ability of America to get the job done by democratic processes.

There lies the real strength of America.

CHAPTER XV

ALL OUT FOR CONSERVATION

IN CHAPTER SEVEN OF THIS BOOK APPEARS THE WARNING that unless we act quickly we may one day—perhaps not too far off—face a land shortage in America.

This does *not* mean that we are in any danger of starving right away, or even in the next fifty or a hundred years. It *does* mean that we face the imperative necessity of doing something about it.

It *does* mean that we cannot go on as we have been and have security for the future.

Here is the state our land is in—the land that we expect to support us:

Fifteen percent of all the land in the United States has been seriously damaged by erosion. What's more important, 72 percent of all our good cropland is eroding now, or would be subject to erosion under cultivation.

A billion acres—half the land area of the nation—today is in need of protection in some degree—and in numerous cases in a critical degree. This includes cropland, woodland, and rangeland.

What the well-dressed farm will wear.

A half-million acres of land are being ruined every year by wind and water erosion and bad land use practices.

There are only 462 million acres of *really good* farm land left in the United States, including that now under cultivation and what has not yet been put in cultivation.

And only 130 million acres of this land are non-erodible: only about 28 percent of the remaining *really good* farm land does not need erosion control and other conservation measures, in varying degrees, to protect it from washing and blowing away!

In spite of what has been accomplished a tremendous amount of work remains to be done. We are making headway with this job, but we are not making headway fast enough. Protecting the *productive* land *and producing on it* all the things we need is essential, and we have wasted enough time getting started on the job.

A great deal remains to be done, but we dare not let it discourage us.

We haven't time for discouragement!

We have time only for work! And we must get to work without delay.

Remember Mesopotamia, laid waste by the Mongols! Go look at the great Mongol Plain, the homeland of those same warlike wanderers! Once fertile lands of great productive capacity—now barren deserts where such life as there is has a ceaseless struggle to survive at all.

It is not pleasant to think that these things might happen to the United States or to many parts of it. It's pleasanter to look at the picture of what will happen to America under conservation.

You can see a land of shining valleys, tree-clad slopes; amply protected forests to care for the nation's needs forever; pasture and grazing land for all the stock we shall ever need; broad, productive, ungullied fields presenting a beautiful pattern with their contour furrows—a new design for farming.

You see a land of comfortable homes and happy people; people living in security and freedom, without fear.

You see a land where the people themselves, through democratic processes, have halted wasteful exploitation and instituted in its place a program of conservation to perpetuate their nation's basic strength.

These are pleasant prospects and we have it within our grasp to make them come true with all they promise in peace, security and freedom.

We Americans value these things—we have gone to war more than once to insure their maintenance in the world.

But war or peace, to maintain these things we must

maintain the good land, the rich resources, which make them possible.

Erosion is still wasting our land faster than we have thus far been able to apply control. We have gained some ground in our fight but we started late, and every day's delay makes the job more difficult and more costly. We dare not lose more time. We must overtake erosion in the next 15 years or run the risk of never overtaking it.

Only by going "all out" for conservation of all our natural resources – and foremost our soil – can we keep America virile and free.

INDEX